USBORNE KEY SKILLS

# Wipe-clean
# Adding

Illustrated by Maddie Frost

Written by Holly Bathie

Designed by Meg Dobbie

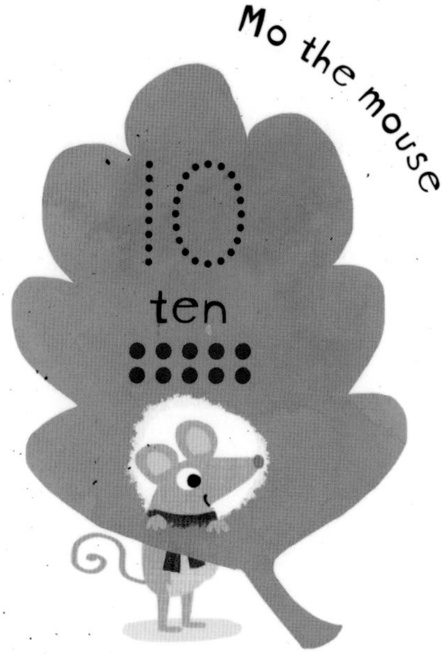

Edited by Jessica Greenwell

Series Editor: Felicity Brooks

# 1 more

Count how many things each animal has found then give them each 1 more. Write the numbers in the boxes.

Squilly
I love acorns.

How many acorns does Squilly have? | Draw 1 more acorn and trace over the 1. | How many acorns are there now?

Mmmm, berries.
Stripe

How many berries has Stripe found? | Draw 1 more berry and trace over the 1. | How many berries are there now?

Squilly now has an odd number of acorns...

...and Stripe now has an even number of berries.

| odd | even | odd | even | odd |
|---|---|---|---|---|
| 1 | 2 | 3 | 4 | 5 |

# Odd and even

Count the other things Squilly and Stripe have found and give them each 1 more. Circle 'odd' or 'even' under each number.

The number line at the bottom of the page can help you choose 'odd' or 'even'.
Olly

How many leaves? | Draw 1 more leaf. | How many now?

odd even | | odd even

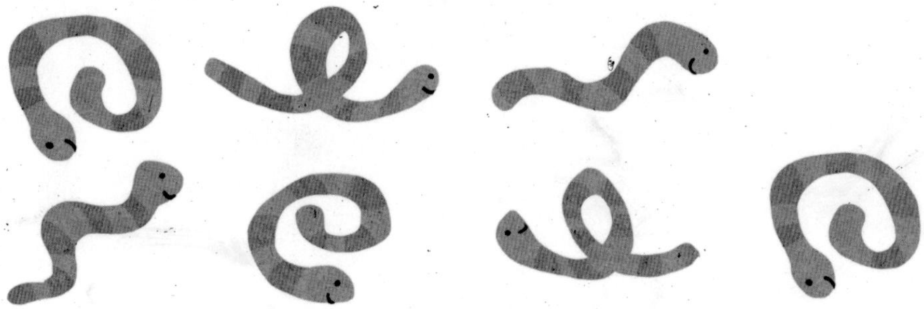

How many worms? | Draw 1 more worm. | How many now?

odd even | | odd even

| even | odd | even | odd | even |
|---|---|---|---|---|
| 6 | 7 | 8 | 9 | 10 |

# Adding more

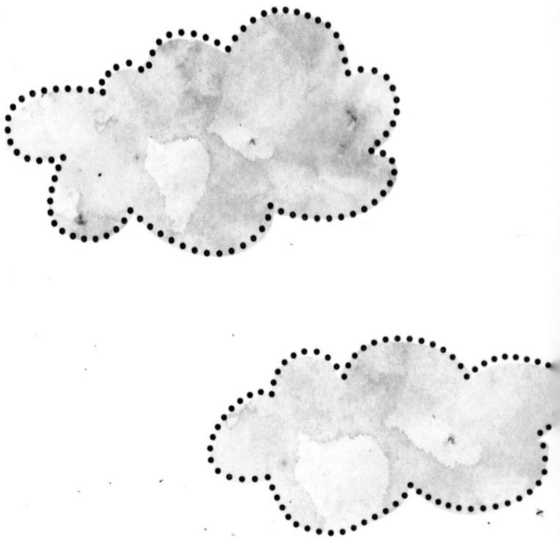

How many clouds are in the sky?

Draw 2 more clouds.

2

How many clouds are there now?

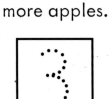

Who wants an apple?

Coco
Bun

Mo

How many apples are in the tree?

Draw 3 more apples.

3

How many apples are there now?

1 2 3 4 5 6 7 8 9 10

Twit twoo!

When you are adding more things, instead of writing 'add', you can use the adding sign, which Olly is pointing to.

**+**

How many trees are on this page? | Add | 4 more trees. | How many trees are there now?

5 + 4 =

Wait for me, Hug!
Hug
Foxy

How many flowers can you see? | Add | 5 more flowers. | How many flowers are there altogether?

+ 5

# What is it equal to?

Mo and her friends need the same number of apples on each side to balance the see-saw.

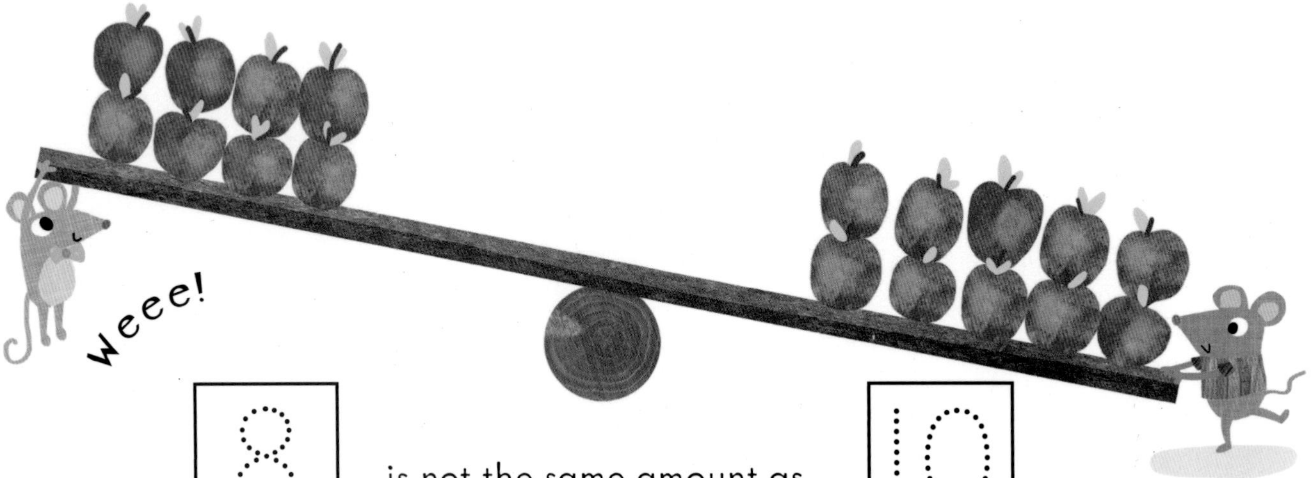


8 is not the same amount as 10

apples apples

The mice have added 2 more apples to make the see-saw balance.

8 + 2 is the same amount as 10

apples apples apples

=

8 apples add 2 apples equals 10 apples. Instead of writing words to show the amounts are the same, you can just use the equals sign. Olly is pointing to it.

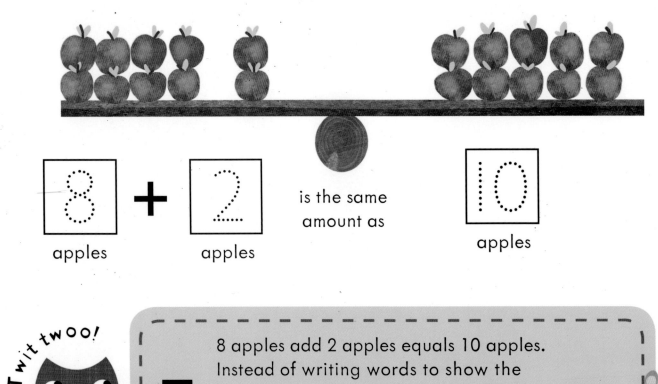

Now the mice are putting apples, acorns and stones on the see-saws.
Draw more things to make them balance and then fill in the boxes.

10 equals = 2 + ☐

10 equals = 3 + ☐

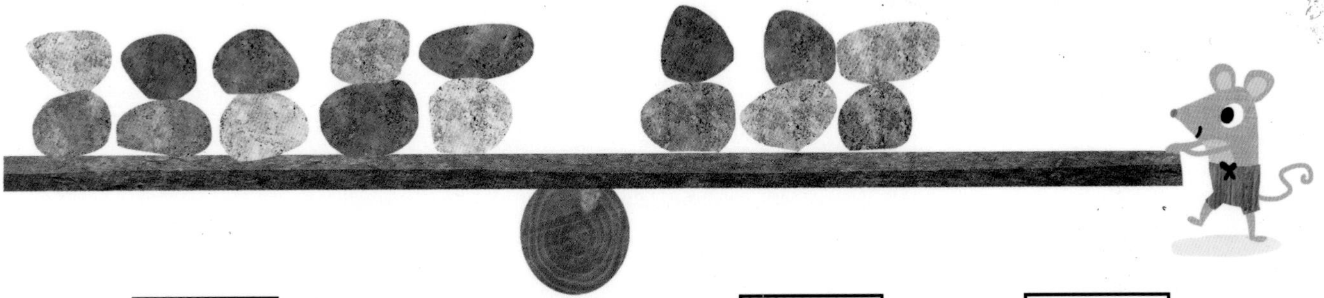

10 equals = 6 + ☐

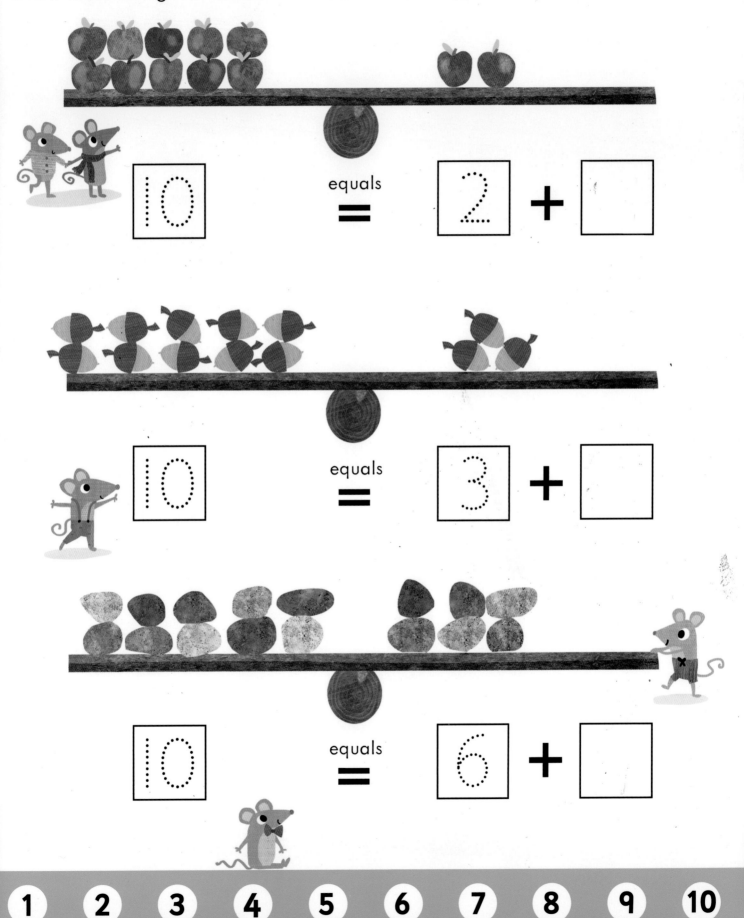

# Adding 2, adding 3

These trains will take Moley and Mo to the seaside. Write how many animals are on each train. Then draw the 2 friends in the windows and finish the calculation.

☐ animals + 2 = ☐ animals on the train.

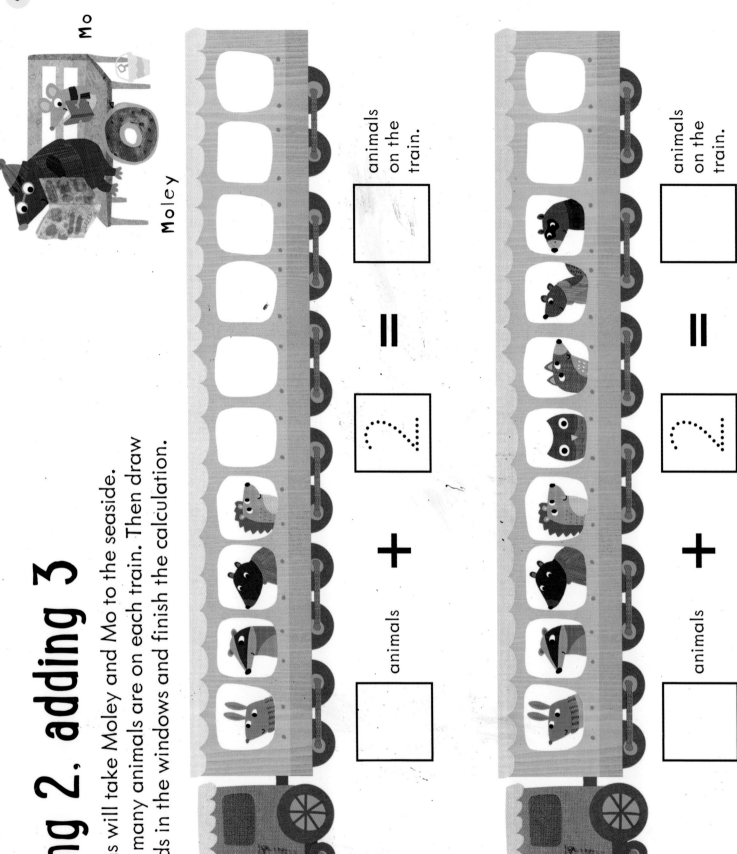

☐ animals + 2 = ☐ animals on the train.

These trains will take Stripe, Foxy and Hug to the adventure park. Write how many animals are on each train. Then draw the 3 friends in the windows and finish the calculation.

☐ animals + 3 = ☐ animals on the train.

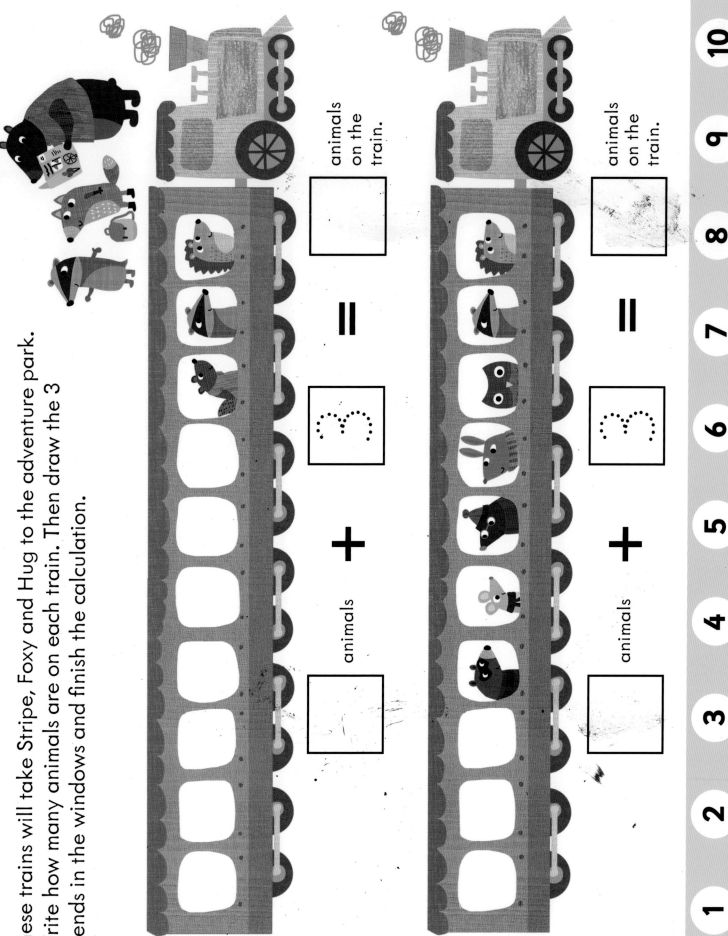

☐ animals + 3 = ☐ animals on the train.

1 2 3 4 5 6 7 8 9 10

# Adding together

The animals need help choosing rides to go on. Find 2 groups to fill the pony ride and draw lines to join them to it. Now fill in the boxes on the next page.

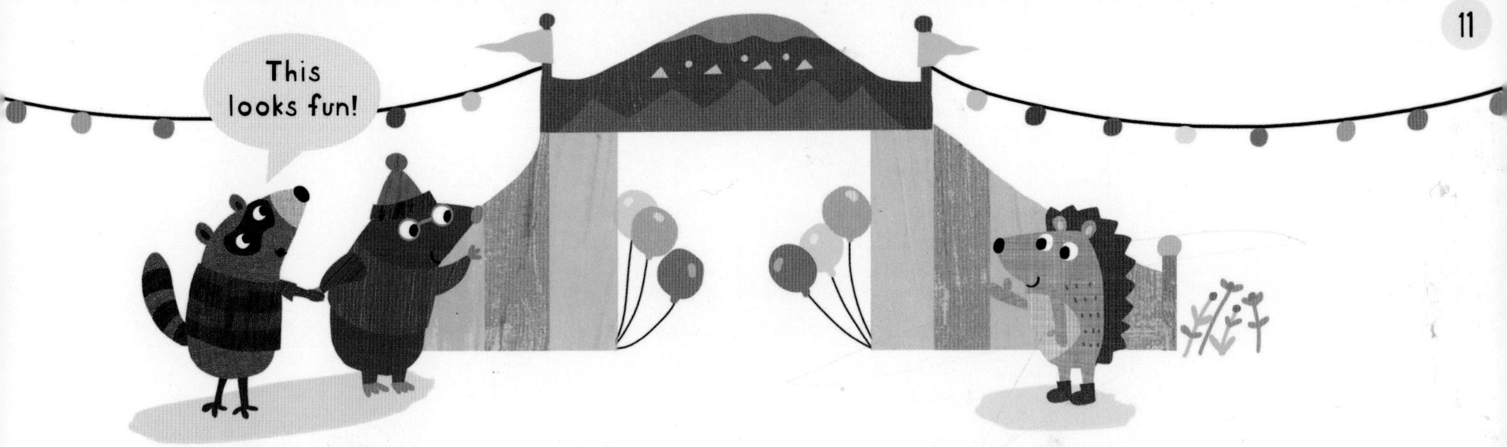


Complete this calculation for the 2 groups you've found to go on the pony ride.

5 = ☐ + ☐

Find 2 groups to go on the teacup ride, then complete this calculation.

6 = ☐ + ☐

Find 2 groups to go on the big wheel, then complete this calculation.

7 = ☐ + ☐

1 2 3 4 5 6 7 8 9 10

# Making 10

Moley has 4 party bags and wants to put 10 toys in each bag.
Help her to start by writing how many toys are in each group below.

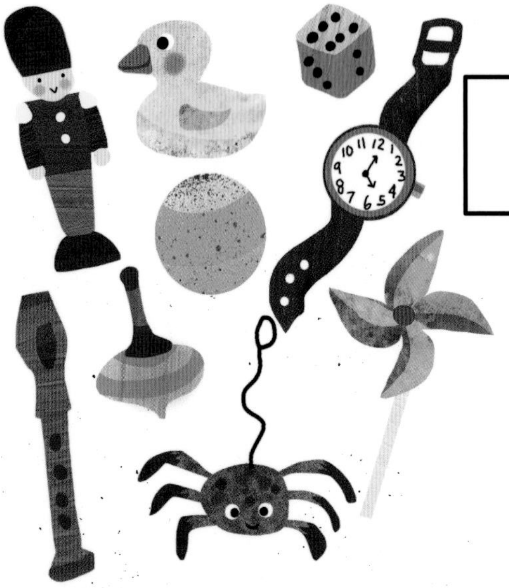

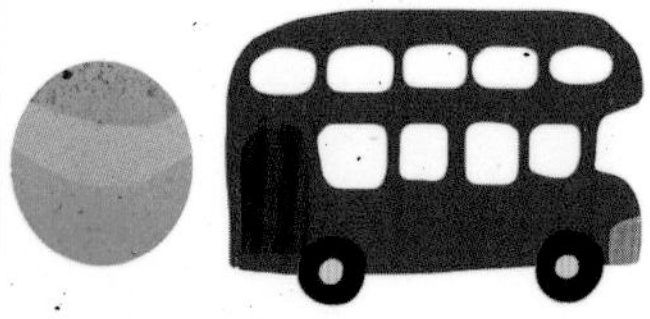

Draw a line to join up 2 groups that make 10 to fill one bag.
Now join 2 groups that make 10 to fill each of the other bags.

Now I have 10 toys
in each bag. Can you
help me finish these
calculations?

10 = ☐ + ☐   10 = ☐ + ☐

10 = ☐ + ☐   10 = ☐ + ☐

Draw another group of balls below to make 10 and then fill in the boxes.

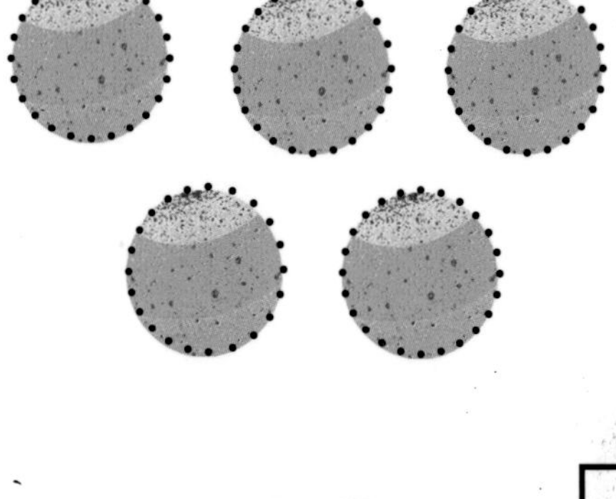

10 = ☐ + ☐

1 2 3 4 5 6 7 8 9 10

# Finding pairs

Miss Bear wants a pair of animals to sit at each table.
The numbers on their chairs should add up to 10.
Draw pieces of string to join 2 chairs to each table.

# Adding zero

Squilly thinks if he adds zero to any amount, that amount will stay the same. To find out if he is right, draw 10 sweets in the box below.

Now draw 0 sweets in the box and write how many sweets there are altogether.

10 sweets + 0 = ☐ sweets

Help Squilly to finish these calculations.

9 + 0 = ☐    2 + 0 = ☐

8 + 0 = ☐    6 + 0 = ☐

1 + 0 = ☐    7 + 0 = ☐

# More than 10

Can you help Mo count how many tasty treats are on each tray in the bakery? Write the totals on the labels.

The mice are buying treats for a birthday party. They want more than 10 of each kind. Draw a star next to the trays that have enough treats in them.

Mmmmm,
these look
yummy.

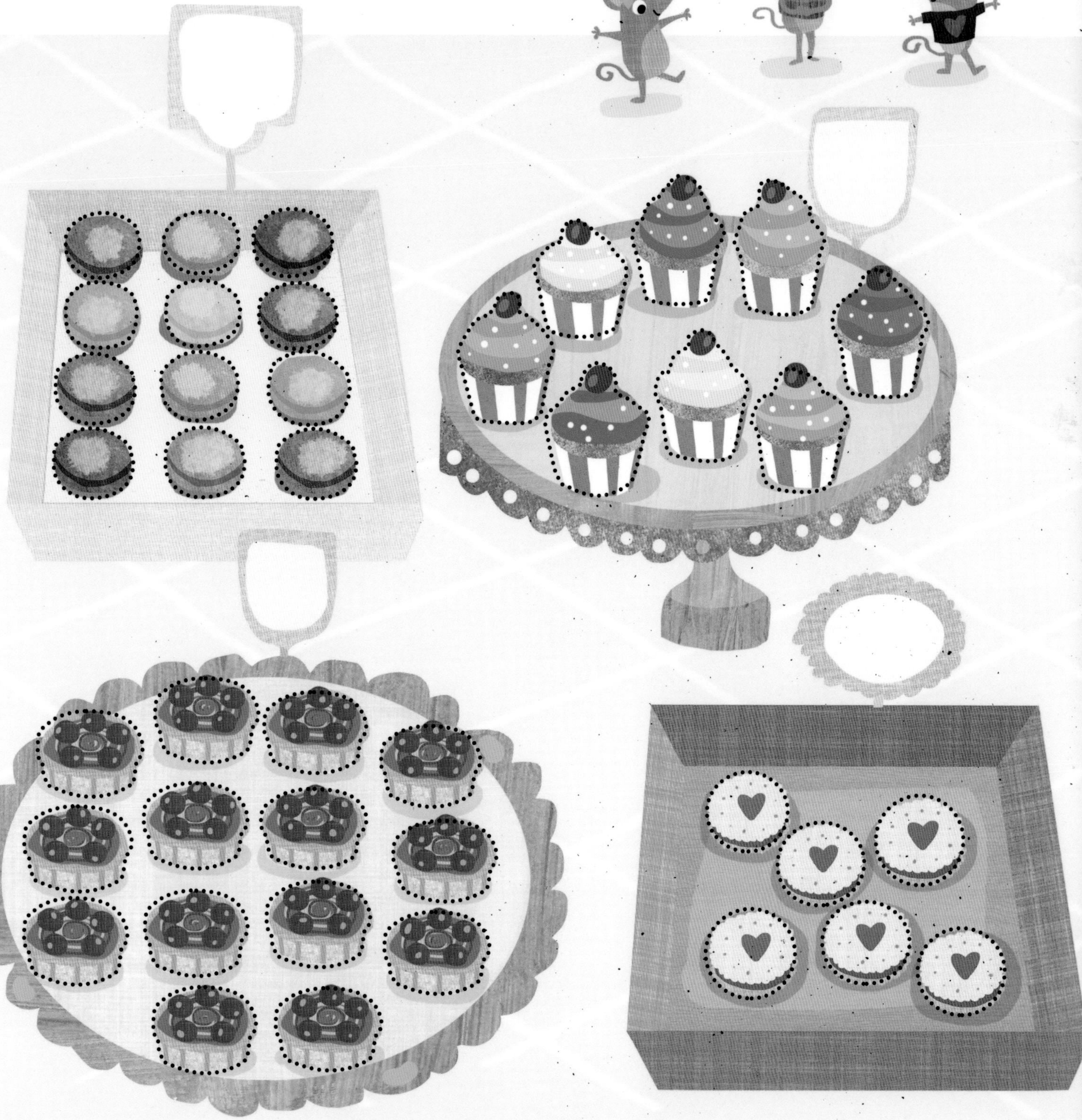

11 12 13 14 15 16 17 18 19 20

# More adding together

The animals are shopping in pairs at the market. Fill in the boxes to show how many things each animal has bought and how many each pair has altogether. You could count along the number line to help you.

How many pieces of fruit do we have altogether?

☐ + ☐ = ☐

bananas apples altogether.

Do we have more fruit than Moley and Stripe?

☐ + ☐ = ☐

lemons pineapples altogether.

All these oranges are heavy!

☐ + ☐ = ☐

plums oranges altogether.

Draw a star next to the pair that has bought the most fruit.

1 2 3 4 5 6 7 8 9 10

Can you help Coco complete the calculations on her shopping list?

## Things to buy

9 + 10 = ☐

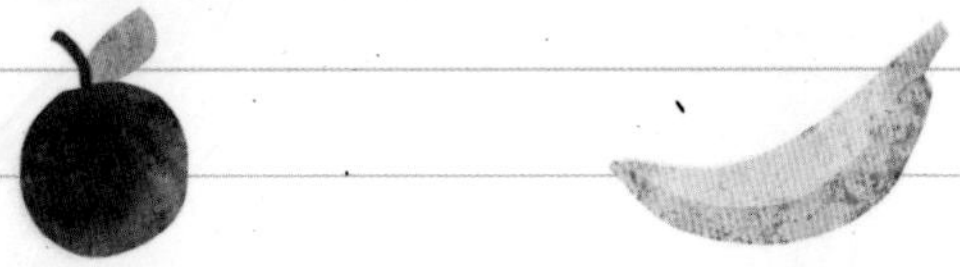

10 + 7 = ☐

6 + 10 = ☐

Good morning.

11 12 13 14 15 16 17 18 19 20

# Number game

When Foxy stops the music in this game, the animals must get into pairs that equal 10. Foxy has just stopped the music – write the missing number for each pair.

The animals play the game again, but this time their pairs must equal 20. Can you write the missing teen number for each pair?

1 2 3 4 5 6 7 8 9 10

# Lots of calculations

Use this page to write lots of your own calculations that equal 10.

This is fun!

☐ + ☐ = ☐

☐ = ☐ + ☐

☐ + ☐ = ☐

☐ = ☐ + ☐

☐ + ☐ = ☐

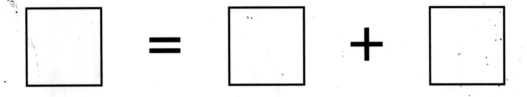

Wipe the page clean.

Now you could try writing some calculations that equal 20.

# Adding quiz

Find out how much you can remember about adding by doing this quiz. Answers on page 24.

A. What is 1 more than each number Hug and Foxy have written? Write the answers in the boxes for Mo.

| 5 | |
| 3 | |
| 7 | |
| 4 | |

| 15 | |
| 11 | |
| 13 | |
| 19 | |

B. Squilly and Stripe need help sorting out these numbers. Write each number in the correct circle.

15    10    3    12    5    9

2    1    6    8

My circle is for EVEN numbers.

My circle is for ODD numbers.

even        odd

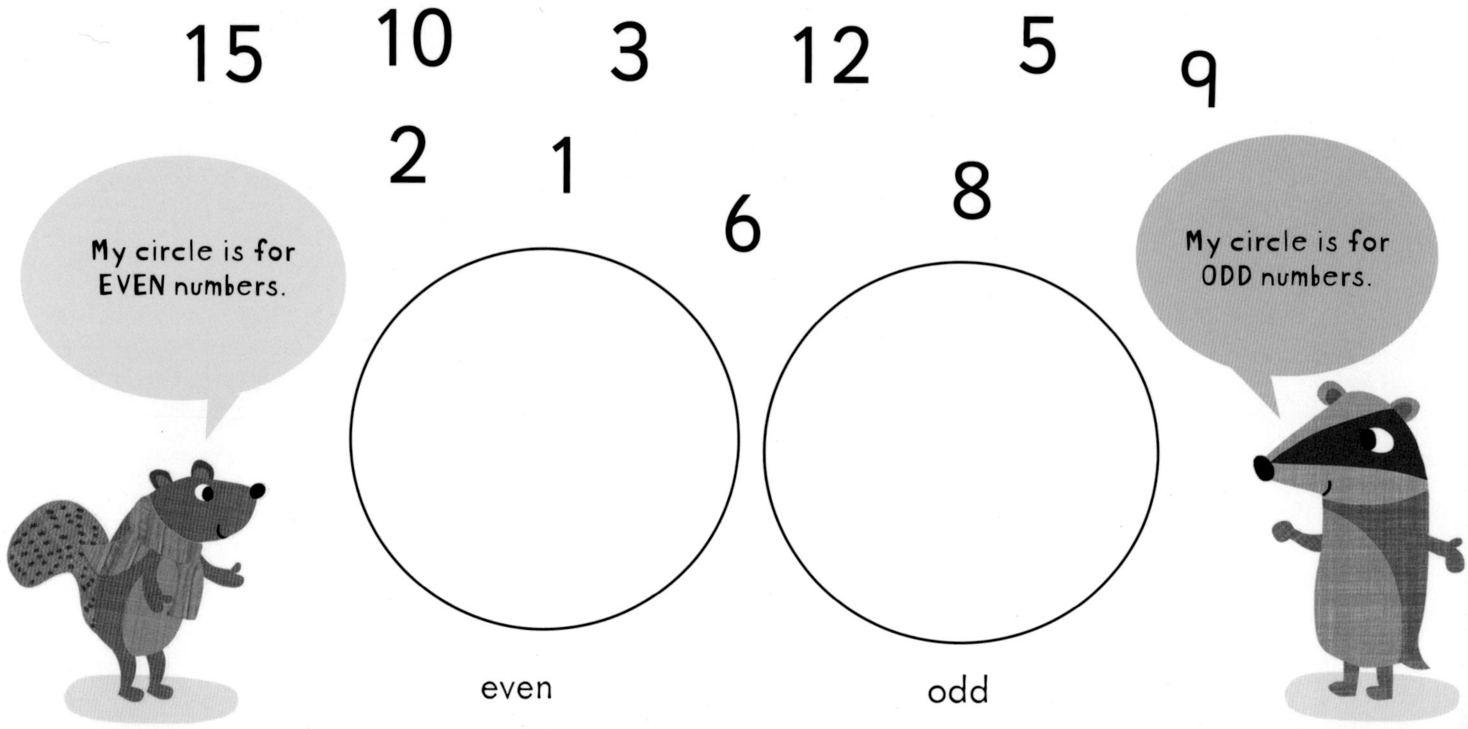

C. Spike is adding to make 10. Has he got all of his calculations right? Put a tick in the box next to the ones that are correct.

| | | | |
|---|---|---|---|
| 9 + 0 = 10 | ☐ | 7 + 3 = 10 | ☐ |
| 8 + 3 = 10 | ☐ | 3 + 5 = 10 | ☐ |
| 5 + 5 = 10 | ☐ | 7 + 0 = 10 | ☐ |
| 1 + 9 = 10 | ☐ | 2 + 8 = 10 | ☐ |
| 2 + 3 = 10 | ☐ | 6 + 4 = 10 | ☐ |
| 4 + 5 = 10 | ☐ | 10 + 0 = 10 | ☐ |

D. Copy the calculations Spike got wrong into the blank spaces below, and this time write the correct answers for him.

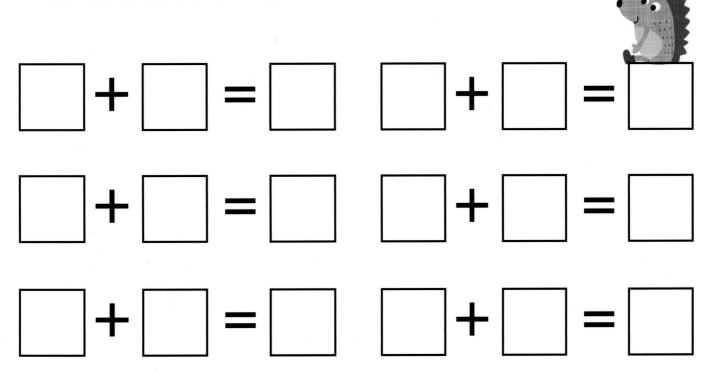

☐ + ☐ = ☐    ☐ + ☐ = ☐

☐ + ☐ = ☐    ☐ + ☐ = ☐

☐ + ☐ = ☐    ☐ + ☐ = ☐

E. Complete these calculations for Moley and Coco.

19 + 1 = ☐ 20 + 0 = ☐

4 + 13 = ☐ 3 + 15 = ☐

15 + 5 = ☐ 7 + 10 = ☐

11 + 3 = ☐ 17 + 3 = ☐

12 + 6 = ☐ 16 + 2 = ☐

10 + 10 = ☐ 10 + 1 = ☐

## Quiz answers

A.

| | |
|---|---|
| 6 | 16 |
| 4 | 12 |
| 8 | 14 |
| 5 | 20 |

B.

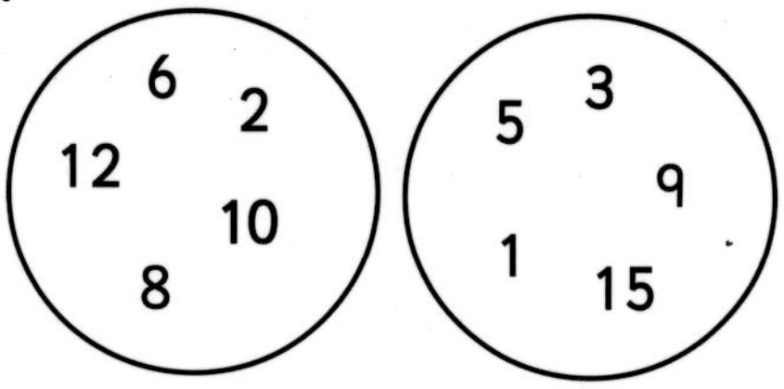


C. These are the ones Spike got right:

| | |
|---|---|
| 5 + 5 = 10 | 2 + 8 = 10 |
| 1 + 9 = 10 | 6 + 4 = 10 |
| 7 + 3 = 10 | 10 + 0 = 10 |

D.
9 + 0 = 9
8 + 3 = 11
2 + 3 = 5
4 + 5 = 9
3 + 5 = 8
7 + 0 = 7

E.

| | |
|---|---|
| 19 + 1 = 20 | 20 + 0 = 20 |
| 4 + 13 = 17 | 3 + 15 = 18 |
| 15 + 5 = 20 | 7 + 10 = 17 |
| 11 + 3 = 14 | 17 + 3 = 20 |
| 12 + 6 = 18 | 16 + 2 = 18 |
| 10 + 10 = 20 | 10 + 1 = 11 |

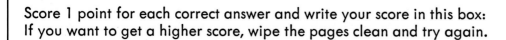

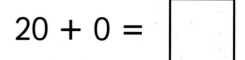

Score 1 point for each correct answer and write your score in this box:
If you want to get a higher score, wipe the pages clean and try again.

____
42